# A Note to Parents and Teachers

DK READERS is a compelling reading programme for children. The programme is designed in conjunction with leading literacy experts, including Cliff Moon M.Ed., who has spent many years as a teacher and teacher educator specializing in reading. Cliff Moon has written more than 160 books for children and teachers. He is series editor to Collins Big Cat.

Beautiful illustrations and superb full-colour photographs combine with engaging, easy-to-read stories to offer a fresh approach to each subject in the series. Each DK READER is guaranteed to capture a child's interest while developing his or her reading skills, general knowledge, and love of reading.

The five levels of DK READERS are aimed at different reading abilities, enabling you to choose the books that are exactly right for your child:

**Pre-level 1**: Learning to read
**Level 1**: Beginning to read
**Level 2**: Beginning to read alone
**Level 3**: Reading alone
**Level 4**: Proficient readers

The "normal" age at which a child begins to read can be anywhere from three to eight years old. Adult participation through the lower levels is very helpful for providing encouragement, discussing storylines and sounding out unfamiliar words.

No matter which level you select, you can be sure that you are helping your child learn to read, then read to learn!

LONDON, NEW YORK, MUNICH,
MELBOURNE, AND DELHI

**Project Editors** Caroline Bingham
and Penny Smith
**Designer** Michelle Baxter
**Production** Siu Chan
**Jacket Designer** Natalie Godwin
**Editorial Consultant**
Theresa Greenaway
**Editor, this edition** Anneka Wahlhaus
**Art Director** Rachael Foster
**Publishing Manager** Bridget Giles

**Reading Consultant**
Cliff Moon M.Ed.

Published in Great Britain by
Dorling Kindersley Limited
80 Strand, London WC2R 0RL

Copyright © 1998 Dorling Kindersley Limited
A Penguin Company
This edition, 2009

2 4 6 8 10 9 7 5 3
007-175923-Oct/2009

A CIP catalogue record for this book is
available from the British Library.

ISBN: 978-1-40534-765-5

Colour reproduction by Colourscan, Singapore
Printed and bound in China by L. Rex Printing Co. Ltd.

Photography by Paul Bricknell, Jane Burton,
Geoff Dann, Mike Dunning, Neil Fletcher,
Frank Greenaway, Kim Taylor

All other images © Dorling Kindersley Limited
For further information see: www.dkimages.com

Discover more at
**www.dk.com**

**DK READERS**

BEGINNING
**1**
TO READ

# Tale of a Tadpole

Written by Karen Wallace

**DK**

A Dorling Kindersley Book

The tale of a tadpole
begins in a pond.
Mother frog lays her eggs
next to a lily pad.

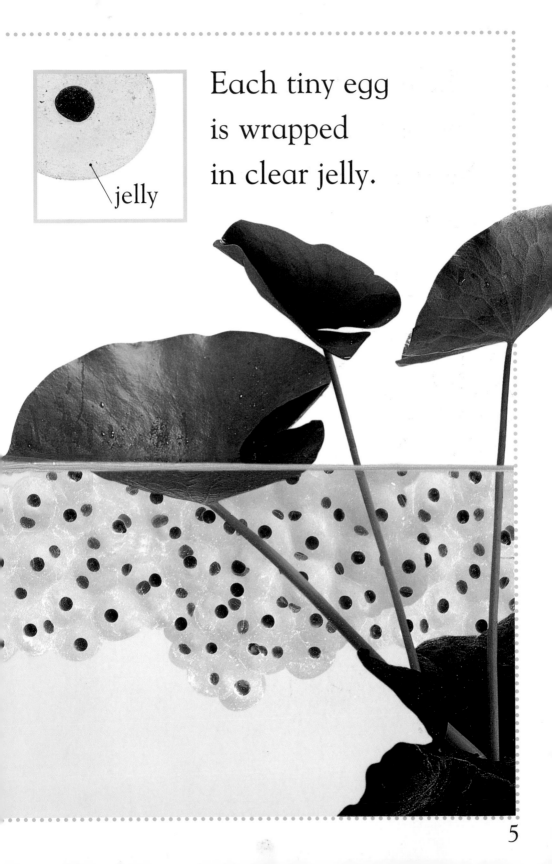

jelly

Each tiny egg
is wrapped
in clear jelly.

Inside the jelly
the eggs grow into tadpoles.
They wriggle like worms.

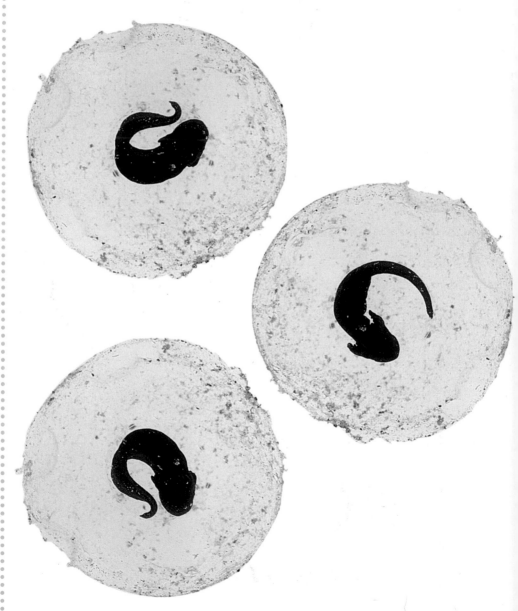

They push through the jelly
and swim in the water.

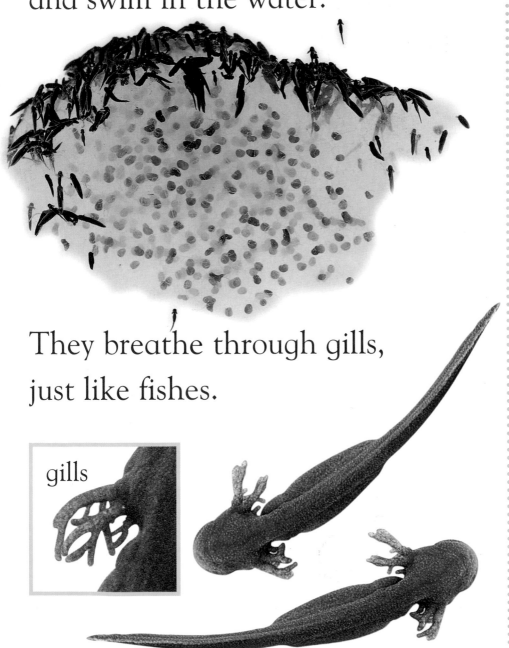

They breathe through gills,
just like fishes.

gills

Many other animals
live in the pond.

There are goldfish and
sticklebacks and
great diving beetles.

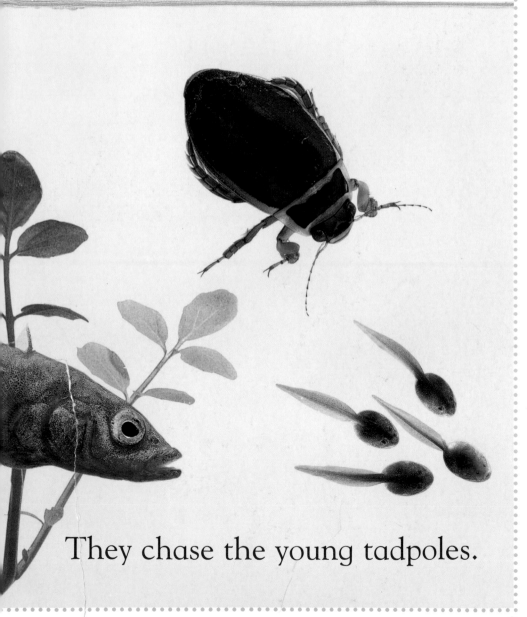

They chase the young tadpoles.

A stickleback feels hungry.
His mouth is wide open.

The little grey tadpoles
wriggle their tails ...

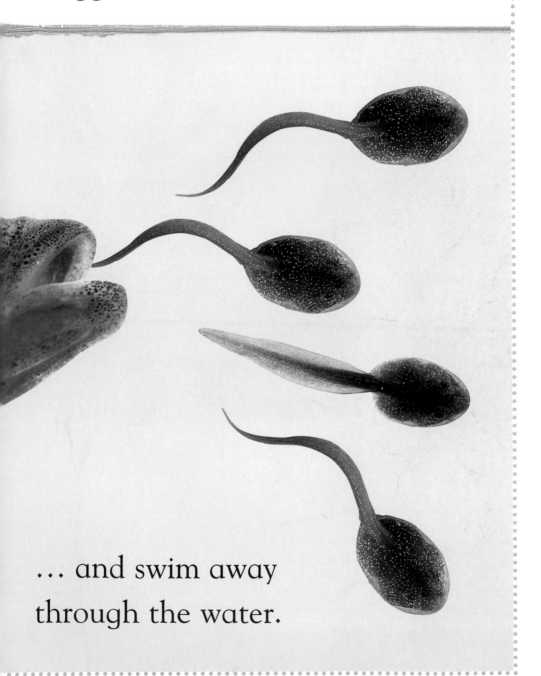

... and swim away
through the water.

A great diving beetle
also feels hungry.

His hairy back legs
beat through the water.

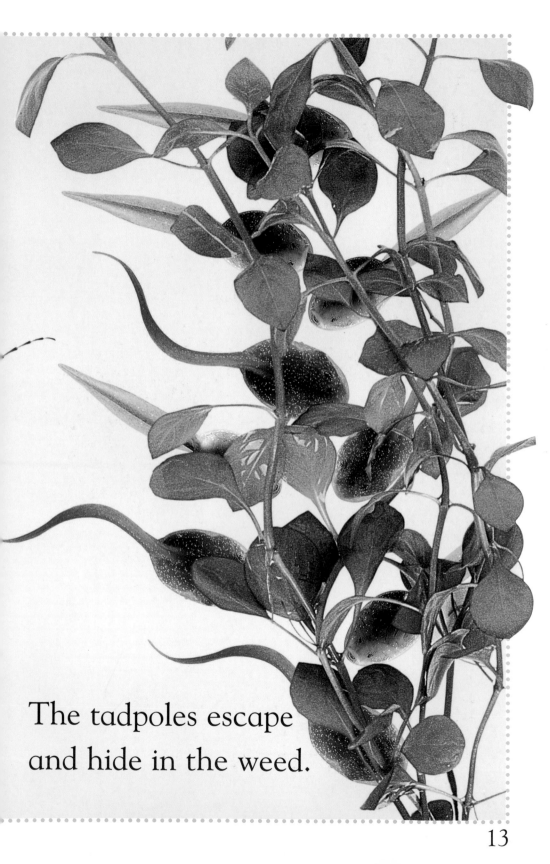

The tadpoles escape
and hide in the weed.

Soon a tadpole
grows legs
with tiny webbed toes.

webbed
toes

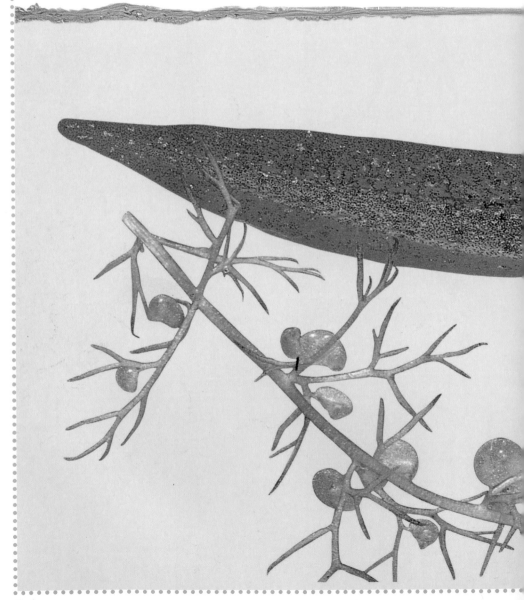

Webbed toes are like flippers.
They help the small tadpole
push through the water.

The tadpole grows arms
with long skinny fingers.

fingers

He nibbles on plants and
gobbles green pondweed.

Half tadpole, half frog,
he rests in the sunshine.

His tail is shrinking.

tail

It gets smaller and smaller.

The new little frog
sits on a lily pad.

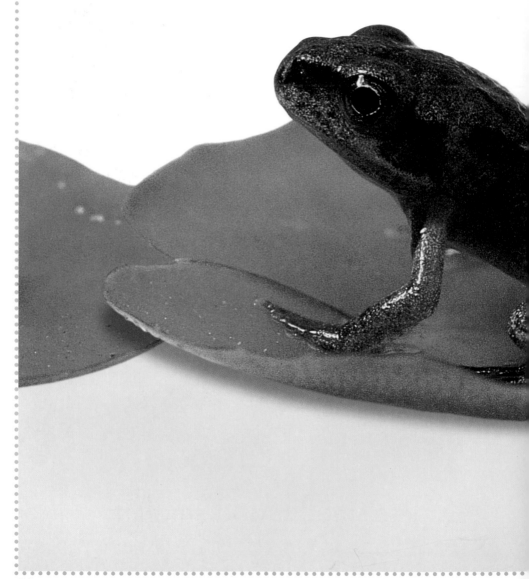

His legs are quite strong now.
He can breathe through his nostrils.
His skin is dotted
with tiny gold spots.

nostril

Frogs must keep their skins slimy.
He hops back in the pond.
He swims for a while
then climbs on to a log.

Another frog climbs up and
sits down beside him.

Now fully grown,
he dives through the water.

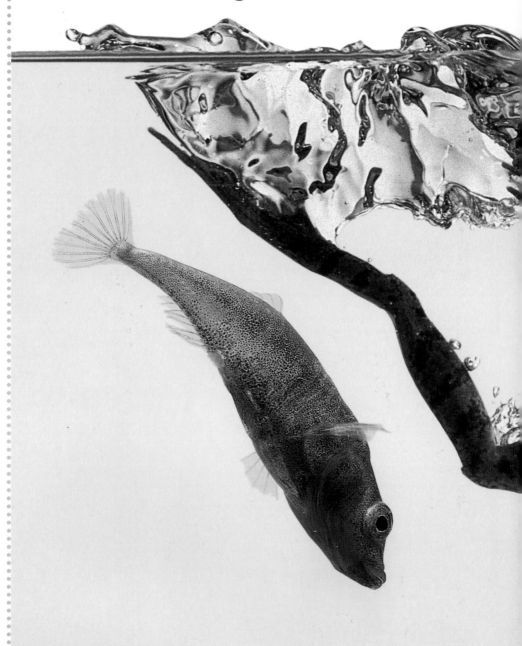

He's not afraid of the stickleback.
He swims past the beetle.

In the pond
he watches and waits.
What can he see
with his round beady eye?

eye

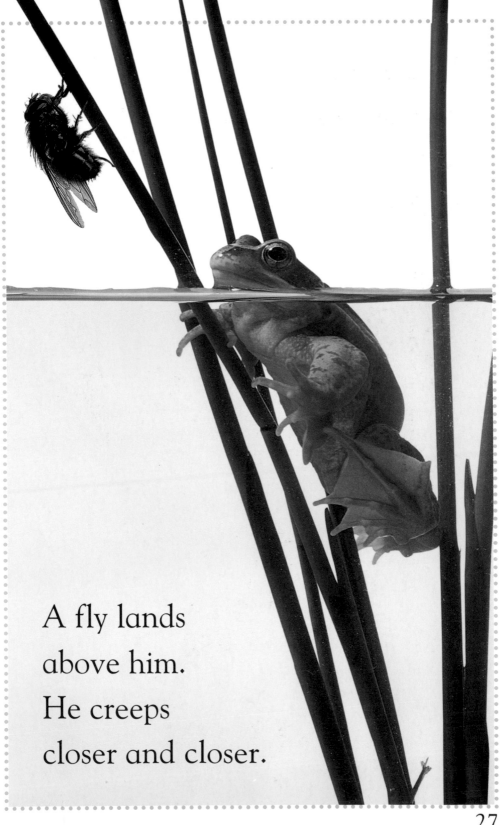

A fly lands
above him.
He creeps
closer and closer.

But a big frog jumps up.
It snatches the fly
with its long, sticky tongue.

tongue

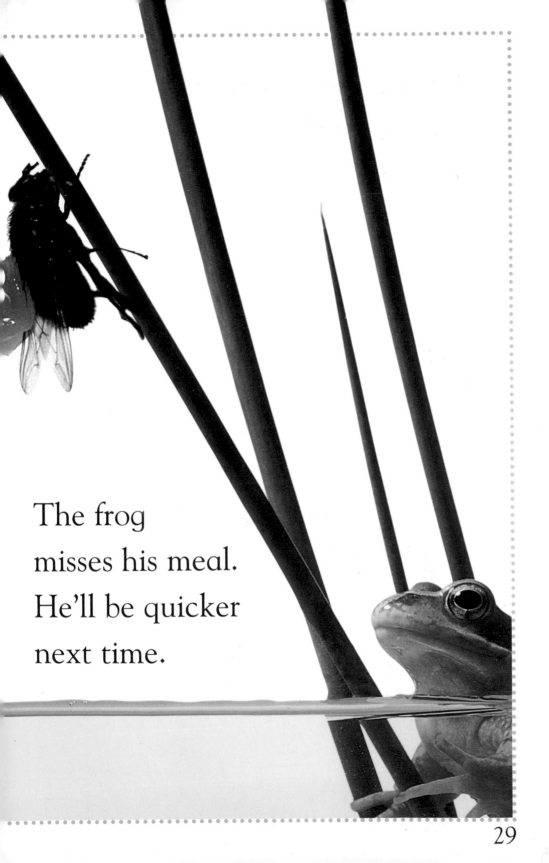

The frog
misses his meal.
He'll be quicker
next time.

The golden-skinned frog
chases a dragonfly.
It lands on a lily pad.
Under the lily pad are
hundreds of frogs' eggs.

Inside each egg
a tadpole is growing.
Each tadpole will grow
into a golden-skinned frog.

# DK READERS

**BEGINNING 1 TO READ**

The pond is full of dangers for a tiny tadpole. Will he ever grow up to be a leaping frog?

## DK READERS

Stunning photographs combine with lively illustrations and engaging, age-appropriate stories in **DK READERS**, a multilevel reading programme guaranteed to capture children's interest while developing their reading skills and general knowledge.

| | | |
|---|---|---|
| **LEARNING pre-level 1 TO READ** | Learning to read | ● High-frequency words<br>● Picture word strips, picture glossary, and simple index<br>● Labels to introduce and reinforce vocabulary<br>● High level of adult participation helpful |
| **BEGINNING 1 TO READ** | Beginning to read | ● Simple sentences and limited vocabulary<br>● Picture glossary and simple index<br>● Adult participation helpful |
| **BEGINNING 2 TO READ ALONE** | Beginning to read alone | ● Longer sentences and increased vocabulary<br>● Information boxes full of extra fun facts<br>● Simple index<br>● Occasional adult participation helpful |
| **READING 3 ALONE** | Reading alone | ● More complex sentence structure<br>● Information boxes and alphabetical glossary<br>● Comprehensive index |
| **PROFICIENT 4 READERS** | Proficient readers | ● Rich vocabulary and challenging sentence structure<br>● Additional information and alphabetical glossary<br>● Comprehensive index |

# With DK READERS, children will learn to read – then read to learn!

£3.99

Discover more at
**www.dk.com**

ISBN 978-1-40534-765-5

9 781405 347655